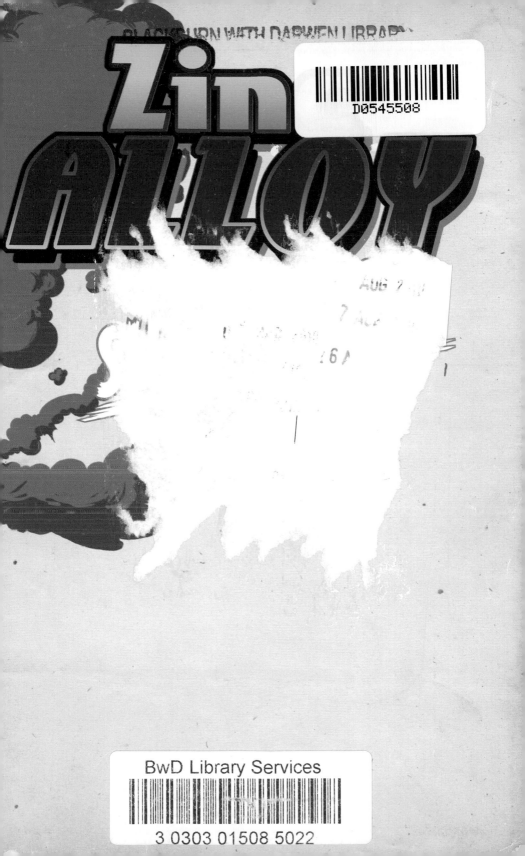

Zin ALLOY

www.raintreepublishers.co.uk
Visit our website to find out
more information about
Raintree books.

To order:
☎ Phone 0845 6044371
🖷 Fax +44 (0) 1865 312263
✉ Email myorders@raintreepublishers.co.uk

Customers from outside the UK please telephone +44 1865 312262

Raintree is an imprint of Capstone Global Library Limited, a company incorporated
in England and Wales having its registered office at 7 Pilgrim Street, London,
EC4V 6LB — Registered company number: 6695582

Text © Stone Arch Books 2009
First published in hardback and paperback in the United Kingdom
by Capstone Global Library in 2010
The moral rights of the proprietor have been asserted.

Designer: Brann Garvey
Series Editor: Donald Lemke
Associate Editor: Sean Tulien
Art Director: Bob Lentz
Creative Director: Heather Hindseth
Editorial Director: Michael Dahl
Editor: Vaarunika Dharmapala
Originated by Capstone Global Library Ltd
Printed and bound in China by Leo Paper Products Ltd

ISBN 978 1 406216 53 0 (hardback)
14 13 12 11 10
10 9 8 7 6 5 4 3 2 1

ISBN 978 1 406216 73 8 (paperback)
14 13 12 11 10
10 9 8 7 6 5 4 3 2 1

Zinc ALLOY

SUPER ZERO

by Donald Lemke   illustrated by Douglas Holgate

Cast of CHARACTERS

Father & Mother

Zack Allen

Spidey

4

8

Several hours later . . .

Yes!

This alloy of zinc and copper will give the suit both strength and flexibility!

BZZZT!
ZZZZT!
FZZZZT!

After all the teasing, name-calling and punches . . .

There, Spidey!

My greatest work is finally complete!

. . . Zack was ready to fight back!

11

The next morning . . .

I hope you didn't spend all night reading comics, son.

Of course not, Dad.

I was working on, er, a little science project. Heehee!

Zack imagined the fun he would have scaring the bullies in his robot suit.

But then . . .

Breaking news!

A runaway train continues to circle the tracks in central Metro City . . .

MUNCH

MUNCH

MUNCH

Its brakes are not working, and it cannot be stopped!

MUNCH
MUNCH

BREAKING NE

Dozens of frightened passengers remain trapped on board, suffering from severe motion sickness!

Zack?

MUNCH!

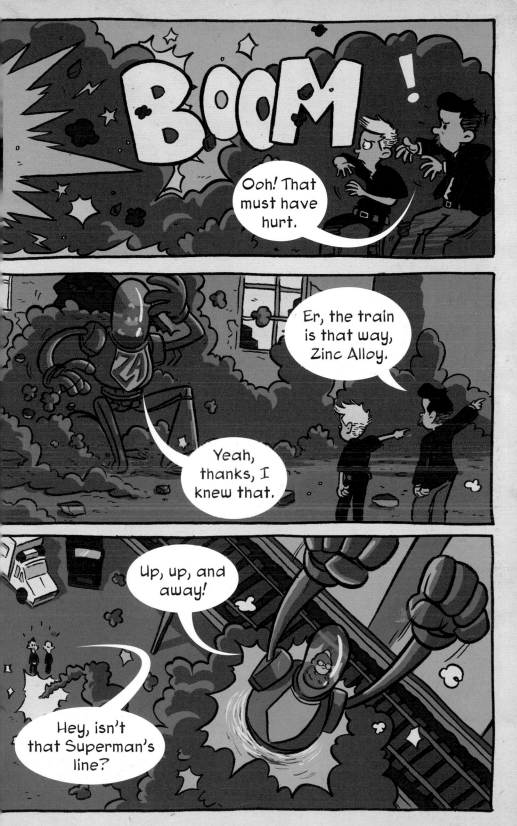

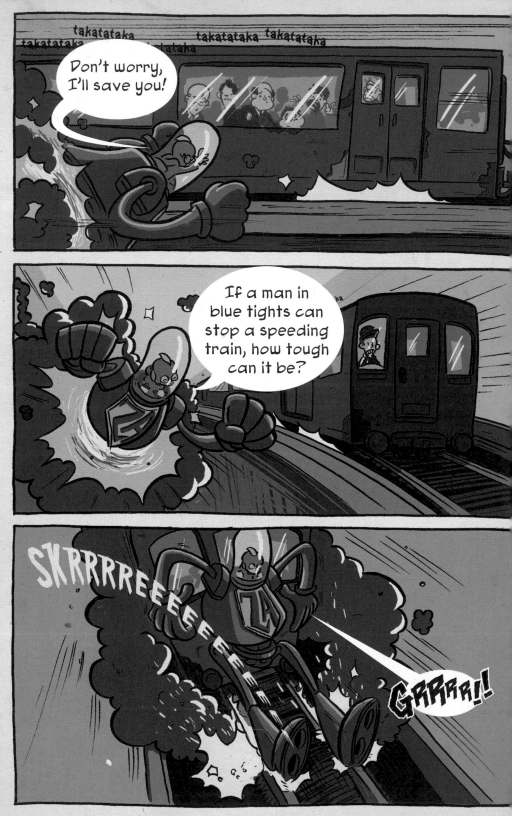

27

About the author

Donald Lemke is a children's book editor. He is the author of the Zinc Alloy graphic novel adventure series. He also wrote *Captured Off Guard*, a World War II story, and a graphic novelization of *Gulliver's Travels*, both of which were selected by the American Junior Library Guild.

About the illustrator

Douglas Holgate is a freelance illustrator from Melbourne, Australia. His work has been published all around the world by Random House, Simon and Schuster, the *New Yorker* magazine, and Image Comics. His award-winning comic "Laika" appears in the acclaimed comic collection *Flight, Volume Two*.

Glossary

alloy mixture of two or more types of metal

clumsy careless or awkward in the way a person walks or moves

construct make or build something

flexibility ability to bend and change shape

reveal make something known, such as telling a secret

rocket booster special rocket that gives extra power to a spacecraft

zinc blue-white metal used in many alloys; iron and steel are often coated with zinc to keep them from rusting

History of COMICS

As long as there have been people, there have been drawings. Some of the oldest are the cave paintings at Chauvet, in France. They are around 30,000 years old and show animals that no longer live in Europe, such as lions, panthers, rhinos, and hyenas.

The ancient Egyptians used drawings for their alphabet. Called hieroglyphs, these pictures were drawn on the walls of pyramids and temples. Each picture stood for a sound, just like in our alphabet. The hieroglyphs told stories, and recorded history and politics.

Comic books as we know them today began in Victorian times (1837–1901). Illustrated story papers called "penny dreadfuls" became very popular then. They cost just one penny and told tales of adventure, action, and horror.

The first real comic book series began in 1884 and was called *Ally Sloper's Half Holiday*. It was meant for adults and told the story of lazy Ally Sloper, who was always getting into trouble. The series lasted until 1916.

In 1937, the first issue of *The Dandy* came out, and was followed in 1938 by *The Beano*. Both these comics had lots of different stories, characters, and pictures. Some of the most popular characters are Dennis the Menace, Desperate Dan, and the Amazing Mr X. Both *The Dandy* and *The Beano* are still published today.

2000 AD is a collection of comics that first came out in 1977. Its most well-known character is Judge Dredd, who patrols a city for criminals, acting as policeman, judge, jury, and executioner.

The term "graphic novel" is used to describe a comic book that is longer than a normal short comic strip. There are many graphic novels available today, some for children, such as *Artemis Fowl* by Eoin Colfer, and some for adults and older children, such as *Persepolis* by Marjane Satrapi.

Discussion questions

1. Instead of getting back at the bullies, Zack Allen chose to stop the runaway train. Why do you think he decided to use the Zinc Alloy suit for good instead of evil? Would you have made the same decision? Explain.

2. Each page of a graphic novel has several illustrations called panels. What is your favourite panel in this book? Describe what you like about the illustration and why it's your favourite.

3. *Robo Hero* is Zack Allen's favourite comic book. What is your favourite comic book or superhero? Describe why you like that book or character the best.

Writing prompts

1. Imagine Zack Allen lent you his Zinc Alloy suit for 24 hours. Write a story about your adventures. What would you do in the suit? Where would you go?

2. At the end of the story, the author hints that Zack will use the Zinc Alloy suit again. Write your own Zinc Alloy book. Who will he have to save next?

3. Many comic books are written and illustrated by two different people. Write a story, and then give it to a friend to illustrate.

More amazing adventures!

Meet Tiger Moth, the insect ninja who takes on some of the world's baddest bugs with his faithful friend Kung Pow. But that's nothing compared to tackling the times tables...